GREAT BALLADS
Playalong *for* Alto Saxophone

Wise Publications
part of The Music Sales Group
London/New York/Paris/Sydney/Copenhagen/Berlin/Madrid/Tokyo

Published by
Wise Publications
14-15 Berners Street, London W1T 3LJ, UK.

Exclusive Distributors:
Music Sales Limited
Distribution Centre, Newmarket Road, Bury St. Edmunds,
Suffolk IP33 3YB England.
Music Sales Pty Limited
20 Resolution Drive, Caringbah, NSW 2229, Australia.

Order No. AM978879
ISBN 1-84449-299-0
This book © Copyright 2004 by Wise Publications.

Compiled by Nick Crispin.
Music arranged by Simon Lesley.
Music processed by Paul Ewers Music Design.
Cover photography by George Taylor.
Printed in Great Britain.

CD recorded, mixed and mastered by Jonas Persson.
Instrumental solos by John Whelan.

Your Guarantee of Quality:
As publishers, we strive to produce every book to
the highest commercial standards.
The music has been freshly engraved and the book has been
carefully designed to minimise awkward page turns and
to make playing from it a real pleasure.
Particular care has been given to specifying acid-free, neutral-sized
paper made from pulps which have not been elemental chlorine bleached.
This pulp is from farmed sustainable forests and was
produced with special regard for the environment.
Throughout, the printing and binding have been planned to
ensure a sturdy, attractive publication which should give years of enjoyment.
If your copy fails to meet our high standards,
please inform us and we will gladly replace it.

www.musicsales.com

Saxophone Fingering Chart

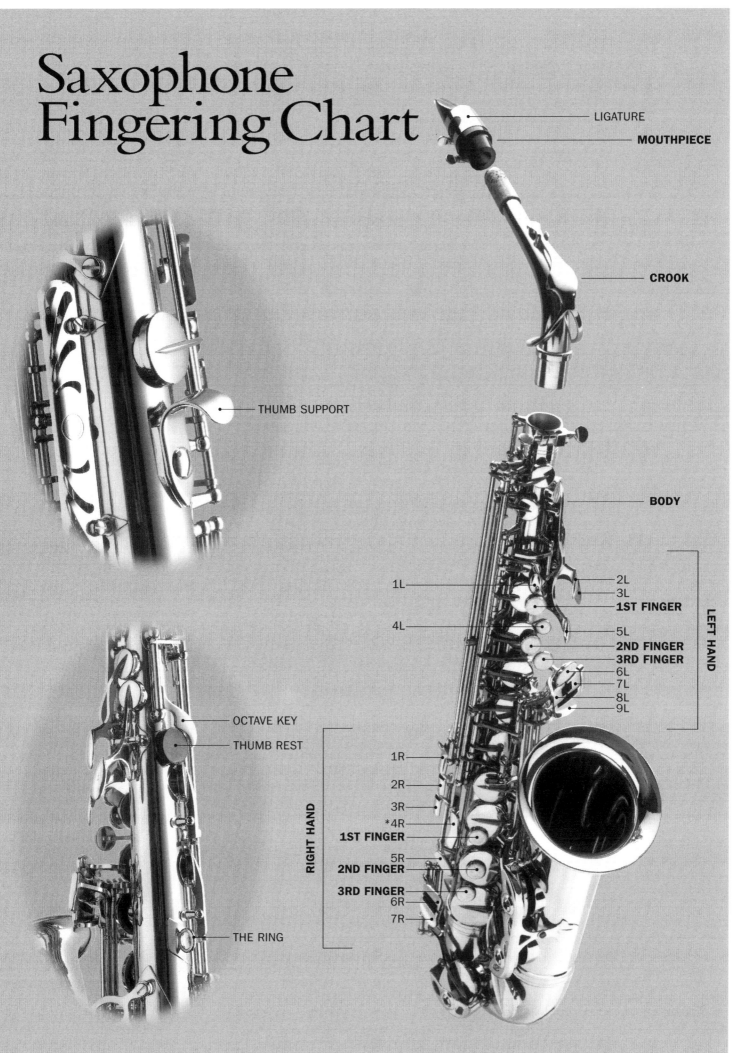

LIGATURE

MOUTHPIECE

CROOK

THUMB SUPPORT

BODY

1L
2L
3L
1ST FINGER
4L
5L
2ND FINGER
3RD FINGER
6L
7L
8L
9L

LEFT HAND

OCTAVE KEY

THUMB REST

1R
2R
3R
*4R
1ST FINGER
5R
2ND FINGER
3RD FINGER
6R
7R

RIGHT HAND

THE RING

* Not fitted on some saxophones

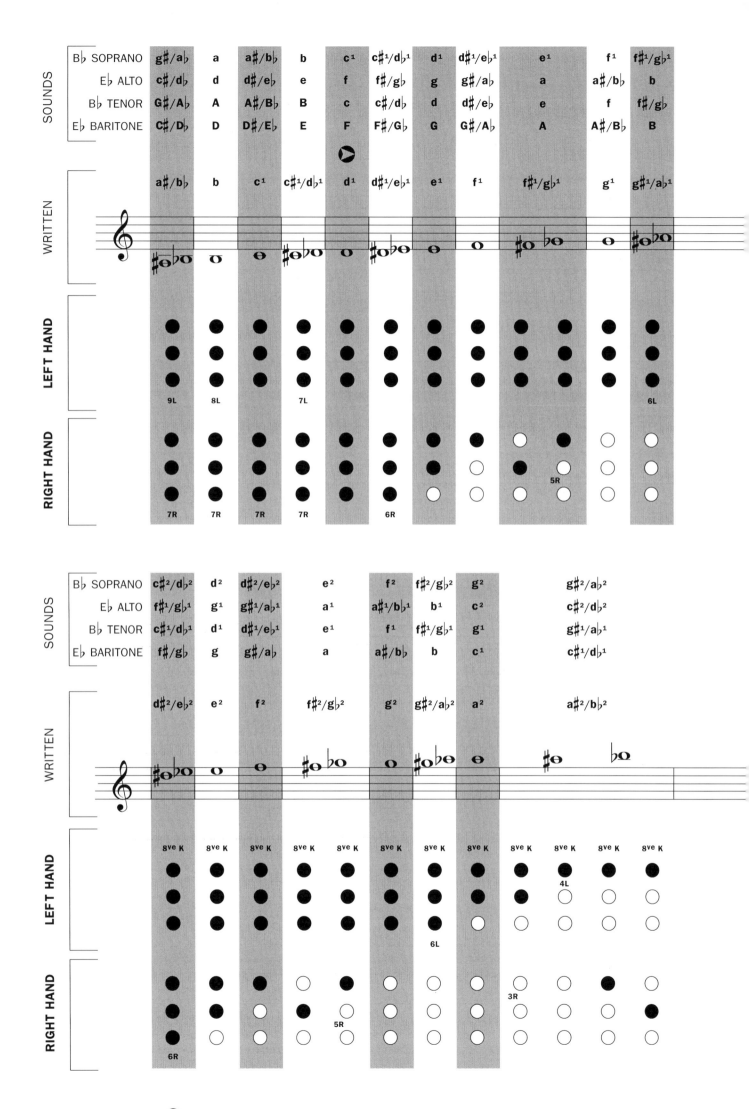

Indicates the lower limit of the best playing range

g¹ g#¹/ab¹ a¹ a#¹/bb¹ b¹ c²

c¹ c#¹/db¹ d¹ d#¹/eb¹ e¹ f¹

g g#/ab a a#/bb b c¹

c c#/db d d#/eb e f

a¹ a#¹/bb¹ b¹ c² c#²/db² d²

8ve K 8ve K

4L

3R 2R 7L

7R

---

a² a#²/bb² b² c³ c#³/db³ d³ d#³/eb³

d² d#²/eb² e² f² f#²/gb² g² g#²/ab²

a¹ a#¹/bb¹ b¹ c² c#²/db² d² d#²/eb²

d¹ d#¹/eb¹ e¹ f¹ f#¹/gb¹ g¹ g#¹/ab¹

b² c³ c#³/db³ d³ d#³/eb³ e³ f³

8ve K 8ve K 8ve K 8ve K 8ve K 8ve K 8ve K 8ve K 8ve K 8ve K

1L 1L

2L 2L 2L
3L 3L 3L 3L
5L

2R 1R 1R

Indicates the upper limit of the best playing range

Against All Odds (Take A Look At Me Now)

Words & Music by Phil Collins

Dramatic ballad ♩ = 58

f molto espr.

sub. ff

Have I Told You Lately

Words & Music by Van Morrison

Tenderly ♩ = c. 104

cue: play if desired

mp legato

If Tomorrow Never Comes

Words & Music by Garth Brooks & Kent Blazy

Soft country-rock ballad ♩ = 80

f appassionato

mf

mp dim.

rit.

p

Can't Help Falling In Love

Words & Music by George David Weiss, Hugo Peretti & Luigi Creatore

In a slow 50s style ♩ = 68

mp molto legato e espr.

The Air That I Breathe

Words & Music by Albert Hammond & Mike Hazlewood

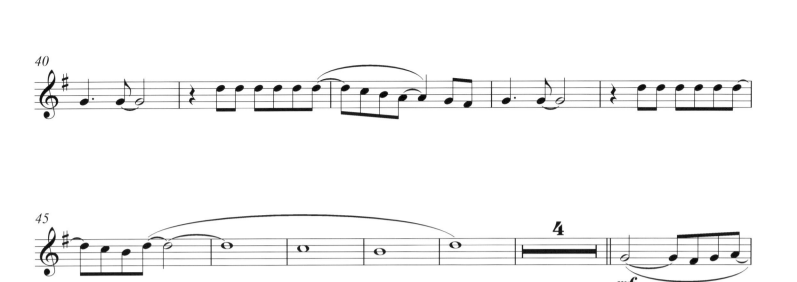

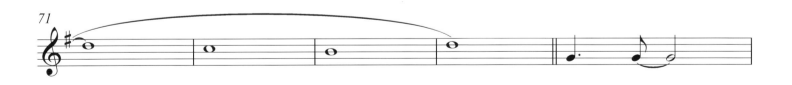

Repeat to fade

Nothing Compares 2 U

Words & Music by Prince

Atmospheric and slightly funky, with hip-hop ♪s ♩= 60

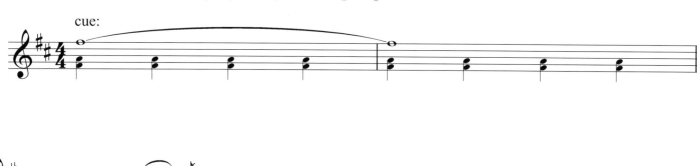

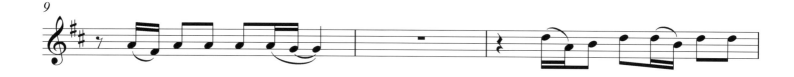

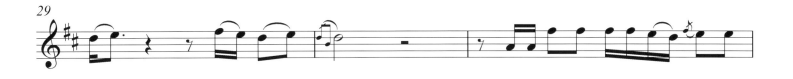

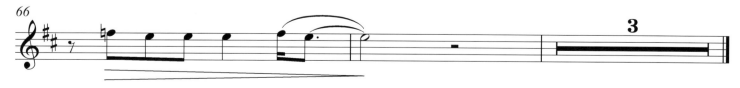

Time After Time

Words & Music by Cyndi Lauper & Robert Hyman

Tonight

Words & Music by Steve Mac, Wayne Hector & Jörgen Elofsson

Sadly, in a rock style   ♩ = 67

Your Song

Words & Music by Elton John & Bernie Taupin

Slow, but with a beat ♩ = 64

mf joyfully

cresc.　　　　　　　　　　　　　　　　　　　　　　　　　　mp

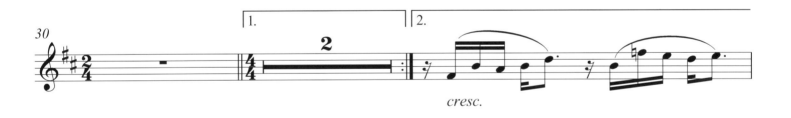

cresc.

mp

To remove your CD from the plastic sleeve, lift the
small lip on the right to break the perforated flap.
Replace the disc after use for convenient storage.